DEDICATION #1

DEAD STOCK

DOUBLE TAKE

$2.50 SUMMO | COAST | DZIALOWSKI | SOVIERO | FLANAGAN

STORY
MICHAEL COAST
MATTHEW SUMMO
BILL JEMAS

SCRIPT
MATTHEW SUMMO
MIKE SOVIERO

LAYOUTS
YOUNG HELLER
JJ DZIALOWSKI

PENCILS
YOUNG HELLER
JJ DZIALOWSKI

COLORS
LEONARDO PACIAROTTI

INKS
LEONARDO PACIAROTTI
ALEJANDRO SICAT

COVER
RUIZ BURGOS

LETTERS
CAROLINE FLANAGAN

EDITOR
CAROLINE FLANAGAN

DOUBLE TAKE

RICHARD BROOKS | PRODUCTION ASSISTANT
MICHAEL COAST | STORY EDITOR
CLAIRE DRANGINIS | PRODUCTION COORDINATOR
CAROLINE FLANAGAN | PRODUCTION ASSISTANT
ALLISON GADSDEN | EDITORIAL INTERN
WILLIAM GRAVES | DIGITAL PRODUCTION ARTIST
CHARLOTTE GREENBAUM | EDITORIAL ASSISTANT

YOUNG HELLER | STORYBOARD ILLUSTRATOR
BILL JEMAS | GENERAL MANAGER
ELYSIA LIANG | EDITORIAL ASSISTANT
ROBERT MEYERS | MANAGING EDITOR
JULIAN ROWE | STORYBOARD ILLUSTRATOR
LILLIAN TAN | BUSINESS MANAGER
GABE YOCUM | SALES & MARKETING COORDINATOR

Dedication #1. September 2015. Published by Double Take, LLC, a subsidiary of Take-Two Interactive Software, Inc. Office of publication: 38 W. 39 Street, 2nd Floor, New York, NY 10018. ©2015 Take-Two Interactive Software, Inc. All Rights Reserved. Printed in Canada.

ULTIMATE
Cocktail Party

Sidecar

3/4 ounce triple sec
3/4 ounce lemon juice
1 1/2 ounces cognac

Martini

2 1/2 ounces dry gin
1/2 ounce dry vermouth
Green olive for garnish

Classic Onion Dip

Ingredients

1 ½ cups of chopped onion
½ cup of mayonnaise
3 tbsps of butter
1 tsp of black pepper
¼ tsp of salt
2 cups of sour cream
1 tsp of garlic powder

Directions:

• Heat butter in a saucepan. Add black pepper, salt, garlic powder and onions, sauté for 10 minutes.
• Mix mayonnaise, sour cream and sautéed onions in large bowl. Serve at room temperature or chilled if desired.

Manhattan

2 ounces bourbon whiskey
1/2 ounce sweet vermouth
1/2 ounce dry vermouth
2 dashes Angostura bitters
Maraschino cherry

Cosmo

2 ounces vodka
1/2 ounce triple sec
3/4 ounce cranberry juice
1/4 ounce fresh lime juice
1 2-inch orange peel/twist

Swiss Fondue

Ingredients

2 cups of shredded Emmental (or Swiss) cheese
2 cups of shredded Gruyere cheese
3 tbsps cornstarch
1 clove of garlic, minced

1 tsp of ground mustard
1 cup of dry white wine
1 tablespoon of lemon juice
Pinch of nutmeg
Assorted dipping foods

Directions:

• Mix Emmental, Gruyere, cornstarch, and ground mustard into large bowl.
• Add wine, garlic, and lemon juice into a saucepan. Bring to a boil over medium heat.
• Begin adding cheese mixture, stirring in between additions. Add pinch of nutmeg. Fondue is done when cheese is melted and mixture has a smooth texture.
• Transfer fondue to a fondue pot.
• Arrange dipping foods around fondue pot and serve.

Deviled Eggs

Ingredients

6 eggs
2 tablespoons of mayonnaise
1 teaspoon of yellow mustard

Salt and black pepper to taste
Paprika

Directions:

• Hard boil eggs and slice into halves.
• Separate yolks from egg whites and place yolks in a bowl.
• Mash yolks using a fork. Add mayonnaise, mustard, salt, and pepper and stir.
• Spoon mixture into egg whites using a teaspoon. Sprinkle paprika to garnish.
• Chill eggs for 1 hour and serve.

Time's up. Hit it, kid.

Ahem... Attention George's customers: the time is now 6:50 pm.

George's will be closing in approximately ten minutes.

Please bring all final purchases to the front checkout lanes. As always, thank you for shopping at George's.

…This is Samantha Stanton, KBRF AM 530, with the latest news from the station that's first on your dial.

50% OFF!

GEORGE

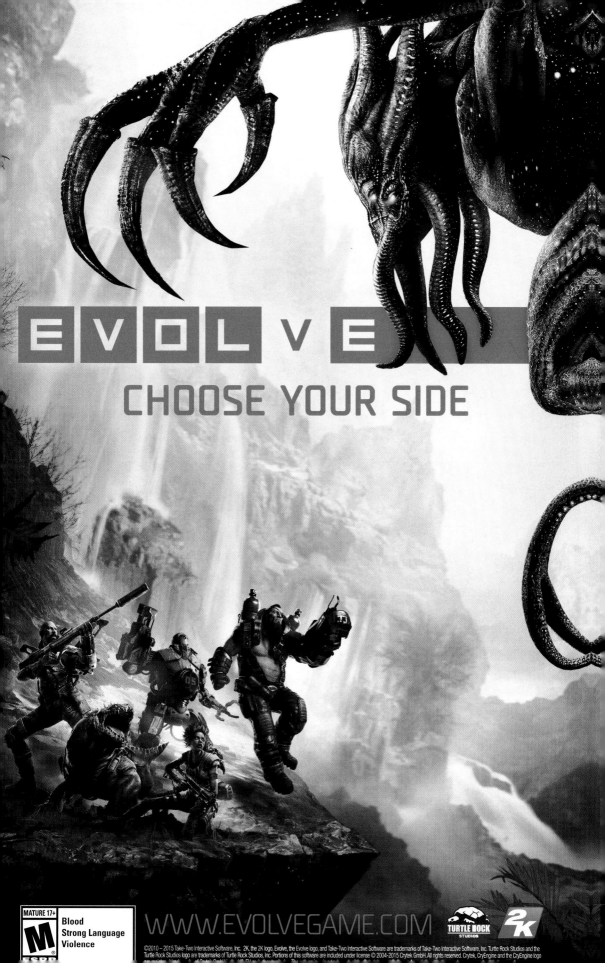

So I'm 12 years old, and I'm stuck on top of my grandma's roof.

And I was in the middle of the ultimate practical joke.

Trip, Joey, listen up.

I need you two to make this place look immaculate. I don't want a single thing out of place, okay?

Let's just make sure all the mongrels have left the store.

...the Evans Dogwood Festival drew to a close under ashen skies yesterday.

...the rain kept the airports socked in so that Senators Joseph S. Clark and Hugh Scott couldn't make it.

And now for the weather: overcast tonight with the sun returning in the morning.

And more information later on the Venus Probe...

See, it was because of my grandma that I would pull these practical jokes. She was the happiest person I knew.

She was the one who taught us how to laugh and to enjoy life.

She would always say, the more you laugh in life, the more life is worth living. And she…

The front door is locked. I'm gonna go back to my office and count out how much money I lost today.

You two finish leveling the shelves and watch the door.

No problem, right? Like chewing gum and walking.

You're my number one guy, Trip. Just don't destroy the place.

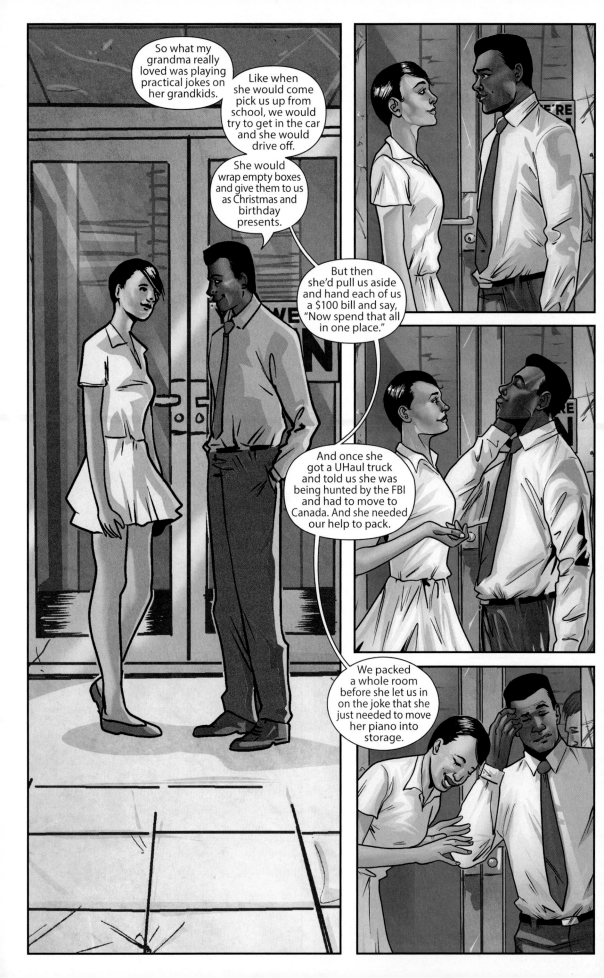

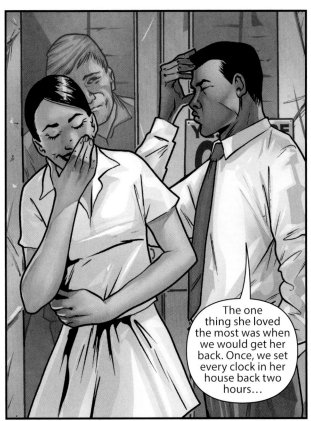

The one thing she loved the most was when we would get her back. Once, we set every clock in her house back two hours...

We're closed, buddy! Come back tomorrow!

Read the sign, guy!

Should we get George back up here or call the cops or something?

This guy seems pretty insistent on getting in.

If we tell George, he's just gonna get mad at us for not handling it ourselves. If we call the cops, George is gonna get pissed that we didn't let him know.

So, I should go tell George that I'm calling the cops? I'm confused.

Just do *something!*

Excuse me, sir...

I just leveled that, you jerk!

CHOMP!

That usually works better if you open the box, open the bag inside, and—

Oh, never mind.

I'm pretty sure you're not supposed to eat that.

So if everyone could just leave without making more of a mess for me to clean up, that would be terrific.

That's a great brand, and they're actually on sale today for—

…free for you, sir. Never mind.

What is even going on here today?

Can you survive the zombie apocalypse?

Yes? You probably think you can.
There is only one way to find out.

Play the **Dead Reign® RPG**. The core rule book, a few players, some dice and an active imagination are all you need to start playing. Rules are easy. Character creation is fast and fun. Combat, quick and deadly. Survival? Harder than you may think.

- **7 different types of zombies. Zombie combat and survival tips.**
- **6 Apocalyptic Character Classes and Ordinary People.**
- **101 Random Scenarios, Encounters, Settings and places of note.**
- **100 Random Corpse Searches, other tables, weapons & vehicles.**
- **Death Cults, their Priests, power over zombies and goals.**
- **Quick Roll Character Creation tables (10 minutes).**
- **5 sourcebooks provide more types of zombies, survival tips, new dangers and adventure.**
- **The Dead Reign™ core rule book is 224 pages – Cat. No. 230. A complete role-playing game book.**

Discover the Palladium Books® RPG Megaverse®
Fun to read. A blast to play. The Palladium role-playing rule system is the same in every game. This means once readers become familiar with one game, they can play them *ALL*.

Better yet, you can link and combine several game worlds to create epic, multi-dimensional adventures on a cosmic scale!

What's that? You've never seen a role-playing game? The role-playing core rule book contains all the rules and data you need to create characters and get you started. Each game or supplement is a magazine size soft-bound or hardcover book, 48-352 pages, and jam-packed with great art, heroes, villains, adventures and tons of ideas. **Dead Reign®** and **Robotech®** are excellent for those of you new to pen and paper RPGs.

Rifts® is the Earth of the future, but a transformed and alien Earth where magic and technology coexist and realities from countless dimensions collide. Alien predators and supernatural monsters prey upon the human survivors and threaten to conquer the world.

Players can be any number of aliens, mutants, warriors, cyborgs, robots and wizards. Lines of magic crisscross the Earth, giving life to dragons, godlings and supernatural horrors. They also lead to dimensional gateways called "Rifts" that link the Earth to the infinite Megaverse®. In **Rifts®** anything is possible.

Unleash your imagination! Drop by our website to learn more about our games or make purchases from our online store. Also available in comic book and game stores everywhere.

www.palladiumbooks.com

DEE!

Trip, I'm so sorry!

It's fine I needed a shower, I guess. I need help.

A bunch of lunatics broke in through the front window. They're eating everything in sight and they won't listen to me.

What?! I'll get rid of these creeps.

Wait!

Dee! Wait! Maybe we should just get George.

Listen here all of you.

I don't know where exactly you got the notion that it would be just dandy of you to break into our store and just eat whatever you want like we're a damned buffet.

I'm here to tell you that it is decidedly **NOT** okay!

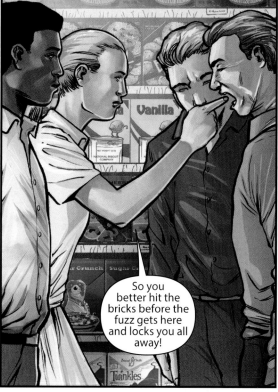

So you better hit the bricks before the fuzz gets here and locks you all away!

PREVIEW: **HOME #1**

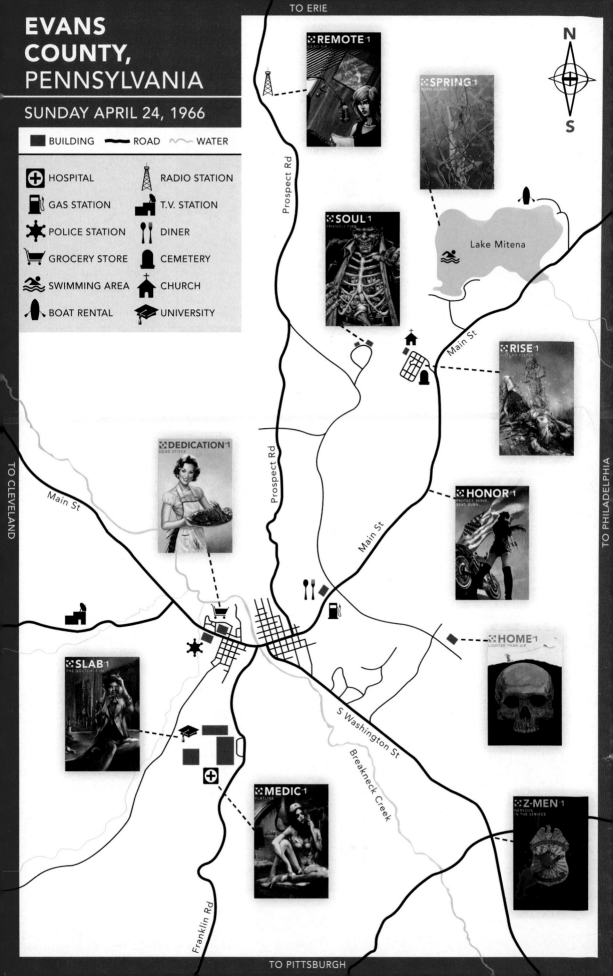